MW00634551

The Tidy Home
Joy Journal

A guide to organizing your home, mind, and life once and for all

I, _____ *commit to changing my*
life by surrounding myself only with the things that spark joy.

Signed:

• •

My KonMari Tidying Journey

START DATE: _____

END DATE: _____

---

thetidyhomejoyjournal.com

Help us spread virtues of respect, gratitude, and joy through tidy living by sharing photos of you putting **#thetidyhomejoyjournal** into action via social media (don't forget to tag: **@fortheloveoftidy**).

Requests for information should be addressed to:
For the Love of Tidy
1658 N Milwaukee Ave #517
Chicago, IL 60647
admin@fortheloveoftidy.com

Graphic design: New Breed Design
Peer review: Heather Young
Copy editing: Ink Blotter Editing
Photo credit: Martine Severin Photos

Published with gratitude and joy by For the Love of Tidy, LLC

By investing in this journal, you've unlocked a
KonMari Action Pack that extends your tidying
experience and encourages you to maintain momentum.
Join **The Spark Joy Club** private membership group
via Facebook to gain access to to The Tidy Blitz virtual
tidying course.

Visit:
facebook.com/groups/**thesparkjoyclub**

If you have any issues accessing these tools, please email: **admin@fortheloveoftidy.com**

How would your life change if your home were clutter free?

Marie Kondo's bestseller, *The Life-Changing Magic of Tidying Up*, sold 10 million copies worldwide since its U.S. debut in 2014. The book sparked a movement that continues to inspire the world to choose joy, and it has already transformed many lives—including my own. However, as I share the KonMari Method™ fundamentals to crowds across Chicagoland and beyond, I'm fascinated by the number of people who ultimately fail to achieve their desired state of order despite wanting to make a change through this revolutionary organizing technique.

What is keeping the KonMari curious from living a clutter-free life of joy? Simply put, it's the inability to step over fear and TAKE ACTION.

In our homes and in our lives, we have the power to prioritize or dismiss activities based on choices we make around our immediate comfort level. And tidying KonMari style, from the inside out, is often an activity we excuse ourselves from because it can feel uncomfortable—even though we know that transformation is merely a few months away. It's time to embrace the momentary discomfort. Tidying is a not-so-glamorous form of self-care that's necessary to create a shift in our mindset and habitual behavior. Once completed, it evokes lasting change across our home, mind, and life.

It's time to invest in change, not more stuff.

I created *The Tidy Home Joy Journal* for the sole purpose of helping you bring the KonMari Method™ to life in a way that breeds motivation and cures fear. The step-by-step guidance, questions, checklists, and resources in this journal are designed to keep you present during your KonMari Tidying Journey so you don't miss a single lesson your clutter may be trying to teach you.

So, stop waiting for motivation to come around "someday." GET TIDY NOW and become an extension of a home you honor.

P.S. Still waiting for the right moment to tidy?
Listen to sparkjoypodcast.com *Episode 37: The True Cost of Clutter.*

How to Use and Make the Most of Your **Joy Journal**

No matter the subject matter, content, or author, the only way to successfully use a journal is to consistently use it—fill it out from an authentic place while applying the guidance in real time. You've already taken the first step, which is your pledge to changing your life by surrounding yourself only with the things that spark joy. Use this journal as a tool and a companion as you make that commitment a reality in your daily life.

BACK TO BASICS

You may be picking up this journal at the beginning, middle, or even the final stages of your KonMari Tidying Journey. Therefore, I'd like to highlight three free resources you can use to catch up on what KonMari is all about:

Spark Joy Podcast: Listen and enjoy while you tidy. The podcast is dedicated to celebrating the KonMari Method™ and the transformative power of surrounding yourself with joy and letting go of the all the rest.

Redeem your KonMari Action Pack benefits:

The Spark Joy Club via Facebook: Connect with others who've made the same commitment to a clutter free life of joy as you move from KonMari practice to KonMari lifestyle. While you're there, check out The Tidy Blitz, a short video course that reviews KonMari fundamentals in a practical way. Visit: facebook.com/groups/thesparkjoyclub

WHERE TO BEGIN

Contrary to popular belief, the first step of the KonMari Method™ isn't taking all of your clothing out of your closet and piling it on your bed. In fact, the first step doesn't involve touching any of the items in your home and doesn't even need to take place within your space. No matter where you are in the process, start your journey on **page 8** by defining your ideal lifestyle and living environment. Get a clear picture; understand the "why" behind your tidying efforts and how the act of decluttering aligns with your core values.

✱ Remember, tidying is a special, one-time event; therefore, it's important to treat this journey as a significant life milestone and capture the memories!

A KonMari Snapshot

The KonMari Method™ is a revolutionary organizing technique made popular by Marie Kondo's bestselling book, *The Life-Changing Magic of Tidying Up*. The method celebrates what you choose to keep rather than focusing on what or how much you decide to discard, donate, or sell.

A combination of Kondo's first and last name, the KonMari Method™ shifts your attention to what you choose to keep in your life by asking, Does it "spark joy"?

Based on fundamental principles of respect, gratitude, and joy, the unconventional KonMari organization process is rooted in Japanese values:

✧ **Vision first.** Ground your decision-making by defining your ideal lifestyle and living environment.

✧ **Greet your home.** Express tidying-related intentions while being mindful and present.

✧ **Organize comprehensively.** Tidy by category rather than by room.

✧ **Surround yourself with joy.** Prevent "clutter rebound" once and for all by only keeping items that "spark joy."

✧ **Handle objects with respect.** Send them off with a "thank you" once they've completed their life cycle.

✧ **Put your past in order.** Honor the things that support the person you're becoming.

✧ **Store items upright and on-edge.** Relieve tension using the signature KonMari Fold.

Marie Kondo's mission is to "inspire the world to choose joy." Therefore, she began to train and certify KonMari Consultants worldwide in 2016. For the Love of Tidy founder Kristyn Ivey is the 12th consultant to be certified by Marie Kondo's organization and Chicago's first.

 Listen while you tidy...

For more KonMari Method™ fundamentals, visit sparkjoypodcast.com
Episode 1: KonMari 101 and *Episode 25: KonMari Myths and Missteps*.

The KonMari Method
Cycle of Joy

Collect and <u>confront</u> one category of clutter (create sub-categories if necessary).

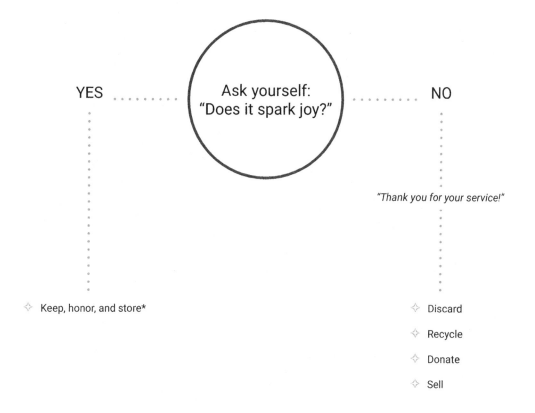

YES · · · · · · · · · · Ask yourself: "Does it spark joy?" · · · · · · · · · NO

"Thank you for your service!"

✧ Keep, honor, and store*

✧ Discard

✧ Recycle

✧ Donate

✧ Sell

*Reuse or repurpose storage items as they become available.
Storage is fluid throughout the entire KonMari process and across all categories.

"Dare to shift your understanding
of what it means to be organized in this world."
— Kristyn Ivey

Visualizing Your Best Life

Unlike traditional home organization strategies, the KonMari Method™ emphasizes the importance of an initial assessment of your ideal lifestyle and living environment prior to jumping into sorting, discarding, or storing your items. This step allows you to clarify *why* you want to tidy and to identify the kind of life you want to live once you've finished your Journey.

 Listen while you tidy...

For more tips that will help you define your vision, visit sparkjoypodcast.com
Episode 5: How to Visualize Your Ideal Lifestyle and Living Environment.

My Current Situation: **Clutter**

What compelled you to tidy at this moment in your life?

What are you looking forward to accomplishing by tidying your home?

How long have you had a clutter problem in your current space?

On a scale of 1 to 10, how tidy are you?
(1 being not tidy at all, 10 being extremely tidy)

| 1 | 2 | 3 | 4 | 5 | 6 | 7 | 8 | 9 | 10 |

On a scale of 1 to 10, how would you rate the volume of clutter in your space?
(1 being minimal clutter, 10 being floor-to-ceiling clutter with limited usable space)

| 1 | 2 | 3 | 4 | 5 | 6 | 7 | 8 | 9 | 10 |

On a scale of 1 to 10, how comfortable are you with letting go of your belongings?
(1 being incredibly uncomfortable, 10 being extremely comfortable)

| 1 | 2 | 3 | 4 | 5 | 6 | 7 | 8 | 9 | 10 |

Considering the clutter in your home, list the five signature KonMari clutter categories (Clothing, Books, Paper, Komono [miscellaneous items], Sentimental Items), in order from greatest to least volume, using your best judgement.

1. . . . .

2. . . . .

3. . . . .

4. . . . .

5. . . . .

My Current Situation: **Home & Lifestyle**

Considering your current lifestyle, what is currently working? Not working?

Working:

Not Working:

Considering your current living environment, what is currently working? Not working?

Working:

Not Working:

My Highest Values

Complete the following sentences. Remember to avoid defaulting to someone else's values or social ideals. This is your life!

I love to...

I spend the most time doing...

I spend the most energy on...

I spend the most money on...

The one way I'm organized in my space or life is...

The one area or place in which I'm most reliable, disciplined, or focused is...

When I'm socializing, I tend to talk the most about...

I'm inspired by...

I'd love to learn more about...

Based on how often your answers appear to repeat, create a list of your three most important values in priority order. This list gives you a structure that will ground your decision-making and help you build your life around what you deem most important.

My Core Values

Example: "Service (loving what I do)"

1. ....

2. ....

3. ....

Is "tidying" or "home" on the list above? Be honest ☺.
If not, you've just uncovered a reason why you've struggled to maintain a tidy home.

Let's lead with gratitude and consider ways you can connect tidying to your highest values above. Write down 15 ways that making the commitment to tidy your home aligns with your highest values.

Tidying up once and for all supports my core values in the following ways:
Example: "Decluttering office-related Komono supports my 'Service' value because I can be more creative and productive in a clutter-free environment."

1. ....

2. ....

3. ....

4. ....

5. ....

6. ....

7. ....

8. ....

9. ....

10. ....

11. ....

12. ....

13. ....

14. ....

15. ....

My Life Map

Mark the scale below to show where you currently stand in each area of life (1 being incredibly dissatisfied, 10 being extremely joy filled). Then, connect all of the dots. What is revealed is a clear snapshot of your current life balance. This includes the areas where you're doing quite well and where there's room for improvement.

The process is meant to be fun and inspiring, so try to keep it light. Don't focus too much on getting it perfect.

Repeat this exercise at the end of your tidying journey to track your progress.

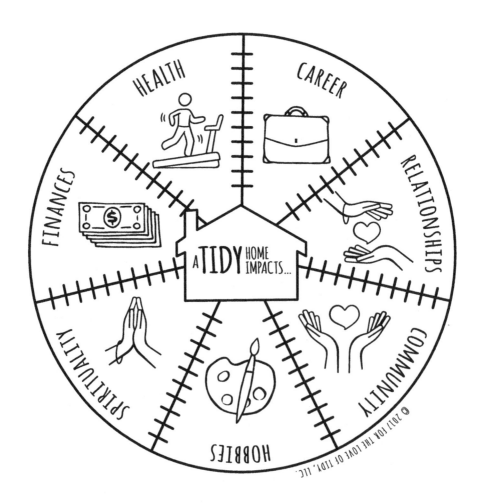

My Future Situation: **Home & Lifestyle**

Think about your ideal lifestyle. This includes the people, places, and things you would like to envelop yourself with to bring you joy. What do you want more of? Less of?

More:

Less:

Keeping your ideal lifestyle in mind, walk through a perfect day in your life:

List the first three life goals (long- or short-term) that immediately come to mind:

1. . . . .

2. . . . .

3. . . . .

Pretend you've reached the end of your KonMari Tidying Journey. Describe in detail how you envision your home will *look* and *feel*, post tidy:

There is no such thing as being too busy or not having enough time.
It's all about what we choose to prioritize. We make time
for what we value the most."
— Kristyn Ivey

Planning Your KonMari Tidying Journey

Unlike many mainstream life optimization tools that feed our culture's craving for immediate gratification and rapid results, the KonMari Method™ is an exercise in self-care and mindfulness that often takes anywhere from 15 to 30+ hours to execute properly. The planning step helps you confront any clutter that may exist in your calendar that would prevent you from making tidying a high priority for the short term in order to yield permanent change in the long run.

 Listen while you tidy…

For more tips on how to plan your KonMari Tidying Journey, visit sparkjoypodcast.com
Episode 73: How to Plan Your KonMari Tidying Journey.

My Tidying Schedule

The average American household contains 300,000 items, and the KonMari Method™ encourages you to interact with <u>every last one of them.</u> The process is intentionally uncomfortable for a short period of time in order to permanently shift the way you view and handle clutter—as well as behaviors that have compounded over decades. Start by confronting your calendar. Ask yourself:

◇ Does my calendar spark joy? Is there clutter there, too?

◇ What activities are showing up the most? Least?

◇ Are my highest values showing up on my calendar?

PRACTICE DEFENSIVE CALENDARING

Schedule a minimum of three firm appointments over the next 3 to 6 months to joy check signature KonMari categories. Tidy no more than 3-5 hours per day. This will require you to temporarily delegate, delete, defer, delay, or diminish some of the priorities filling up your calendar.

Tidying time may vary based on the following factors:

◇ The size of your home

◇ The volume of your clutter

◇ The anticipated pace of your decision-making

Check a minimum of six days over the next 3 to 6 months that you can partially dedicate to your KonMari Tidying Journey.

"What things will bring you joy if you keep them as part of your life?"
— Marie Kondo

· ·

Clothing

Now that you've visualized your best life and have planned your journey, it's time to start tidying. From this point forward, the KonMari Method™ category order is very important and intentional. It is crucial to follow the correct tidying order: Clothing, Books, Paper, Komono [miscellaneous items], Sentimental Items. When you evaluate your clothing, you will begin to practice and hone your ability to distinguish what sparks joy.

 Listen while you tidy...

For more tips to help you joy check the clothing category, visit sparkjoypodcast.com
Episodes 38-40: Closet Joy Part I-III.

Take Action

☐ **Pile** collected items in one place in your home.

☐ **Subcategorize** to avoid feeling overwhelmed. For example:

- Tops (shirts, sweaters, etc.)
- Bottoms (pants, skirts, etc.)
- Clothes that are most likely hung (jackets, coats, suits, etc.)
- Socks
- Underwear
- Clothes for special events (swimsuits, resort wear, costumes, uniforms)
- Bags (handbags, messenger bags, etc.)
- Accessories (scarves, belts, hats)
- Shoes
- Jewelry

☐ **Choose** what sparks joy and send everything else off with a "thank you"

☐ **Fold** items using the signature KonMari folding technique

☐ **Hang** items that look happier when hung

☐ **Store** items that spark joy (until the final category of your KonMari Tidying Journey is complete, all storage is considered temporary and flexible)

☐ **Gather** sentimental items from this category and save decision making for later

☐ **Collect** unused boxes and objects that can be creatively repurposed for storage or decor

☐ **Discard/recycle/donate/sell** items that don't spark joy

 Need additional assistance with folding?

Download the **KonMari Fold Drawer Liner** available at fortheloveoftidy.com/folding-sheet

Clothing Action Items

Things that Spark Joy for Me	Things that DON'T Spark Joy for Me

What did my clutter teach me today?

MINDFUL TO-DO'S

☐ Complete activities related to letting go of "joyless" items (listen to sparkjoypodcast.com *Episodes 42-44: Sell Your Clutter Part I-III* for tips)

☐

☐

MINDFUL SHOPPING LIST

☐

☐

☐

☐

☐

Assessment (Clothing)

On a scale of 1 to 10, how do you feel overall about your productivity?
(1 being not productive at all, 10 being extremely productive)

1 2 3 4 5 6 7 8 9 10

Are you happy with the progress you've made?

What was the most memorable part of joy checking CLOTHING?

What were the three biggest lessons you've learned by exploring CLOTHING?

What sparked the most joy today?

How are you feeling physically? Emotionally? Mentally?

How are you feeling about your ideal lifestyle? Does that vision seem clearer/more attainable now that you've chosen CLOTHING that sparks joy?

Other notes (jot down thoughts that may present themselves in the coming days):

CLOTHING BEFORE & AFTER PHOTOS

"The room you make by discarding books seems to create space
for an equivalent volume of new information."
— Marie Kondo

· ·

Books

Tidying up your books is another great way to increase your sensitivity to joy, improve your ability to take action, and increase your awareness of what you're naturally passionate about.

 Listen while you tidy...

For more tips that will help you joy check books, visit sparkjoypodcast.com
Episode 57: KonMari Books Category.

Take Action

- ☐ **Pile** collected items in one place in your home

- ☐ **Subcategorize** to avoid feeling overwhelmed. For example:
    - General (pleasure reading)
    - Practical (references, cookbooks)
    - Visual (photo albums, coffee-table books, etc.)
    - Magazines

- ☐ **Choose** what sparks joy and send everything else off with a "thank you"

- ☐ **Store** items that spark joy (until the final category of your KonMari Tidying Journey is complete, all storage is considered temporary and flexible)

- ☐ **Gather** sentimental items from this category and save decision-making for later

- ☐ **Collect** unused boxes and objects that can be creatively repurposed for storage or decor

- ☐ **Discard/recycle/donate/sell** items that don't spark joy

Books Action Items

Things that Spark Joy for Me	Things that DON'T Spark Joy for Me

What did my clutter teach me today?

MINDFUL TO-DO'S

☐ Complete activities related to letting go of "joyless" items (listen to sparkjoypodcast.com *Episodes 42-44: Sell Your Clutter Part I-III* for tips)

☐

☐

MINDFUL SHOPPING LIST

☐

☐

☐

☐

☐

Assessment (Books)

On a scale of 1 to 10, how do you feel overall about your productivity?
(1 being not productive at all, 10 being extremely productive)

| 1 | 2 | 3 | 4 | 5 | 6 | 7 | 8 | 9 | 10 |

Are you happy with the progress you've made?

What was the most memorable part of joy checking BOOKS?

What were the three biggest lessons you've learned by exploring BOOKS?

What sparked the most joy today?

How are you feeling physically? Emotionally? Mentally?

How are you feeling about your ideal lifestyle? Does that vision seem clearer/more attainable now that you've chosen BOOKS that spark joy?

Other notes (jot down thoughts that may present themselves in the coming days):

BOOKS BEFORE & AFTER PHOTOS

"My basic principle for sorting papers is to throw them all away."
— Marie Kondo

. . . .

Papers

A single sheet of paper takes up almost no room, which makes it very easy to accumulate far more than you realize. Approach the selection process with the commitment of getting rid of all papers that don't have a clear purpose. Keep only those you're currently using, those you'll need for a limited period, and those that you need to keep indefinitely.

 Listen while you tidy...

For more tips that will help you joy check papers, visit sparkjoypodcast.com
Episode 45: KonMari Paper Category: Cutting Paper Clutter.

Take Action

☐ **Pile** collected items in one place in your home

☐ **Subcategorize** to avoid feeling overwhelmed. For example:

- Receipts
- Warranties
- Manuals
- Coupons
- Recipes
- Pay stubs
- Birth/marriage certificates
- Checkbooks
- Business cards
- Taxes
- Bills
- Insurance
- Notes (classes, conferences, to-do lists, etc.)
- Unused greeting cards, journals, or stationary

☐ **Choose** what sparks joy and send everything else off with a "thank you"

☐ **File** the papers that spark joy across the following categories:

- Needs attention (pending action items to address immediately)
- Should be saved for a limited period of time (contractual documents, etc.)
- Should be saved indefinitely (legal/estate/government-issued documents, etc.)

☐ **Store** items that spark joy (until the final category of your KonMari Tidying Journey is complete, all storage is considered temporary and flexible)

☐ **Gather** sentimental items from this category and save decision-making for later

☐ **Collect** unused boxes and objects that can be creatively repurposed for storage or decor

☐ **Discard/recycle/donate/sell** items that don't spark joy

Assessment (Papers)

On a scale of 1 to 10, how do you feel overall about your productivity?
(1 being not productive at all, 10 being extremely productive)

| 1 | 2 | 3 | 4 | 5 | 6 | 7 | 8 | 9 | 10 |

Are you happy with the progress you've made?

What was the most memorable part of joy checking PAPERS?

What were the three biggest lessons you've learned by exploring PAPERS?

What sparked the most joy today?

How are you feeling physically? Emotionally? Mentally?

How are you feeling about your ideal lifestyle? Does that vision seem clearer/more attainable now that you've chosen PAPERS that spark joy?

Other notes (jot down thoughts that may present themselves in the coming days):

Papers Action Items

Things that Spark Joy for Me	Things that DON'T Spark Joy for Me

What did my clutter teach me today?

MINDFUL TO-DO'S

☐ Complete activities related to letting go of "joyless" items (listen to sparkjoypodcast.com *Episodes 42-44: Sell Your Clutter Part I-III* for tips)

☐

☐

MINDFUL SHOPPING LIST

☐

☐

☐

☐

☐

PAPERS BEFORE & AFTER PHOTOS

"Keep things because you love them - not just because."
— Marie Kondo

··

Komono
(miscellaneous items)

Miscellaneous items play an important part in supporting your life and deserve to be handled and sorted properly. Unlike clothing, books, and papers, this category includes a diverse range of items that may be heavily commingled within your space.

 Listen while you tidy...

For more tips that will help you joy check Komono, visit sparkjoypodcast.com
Episode 61: KonMari Komono Category: Confronting Miscellaneous Items.

Take Action

☐ **Subcategorize** to avoid feeling overwhelmed. For example:

- CDs, DVDs
- Skin-care products
- Makeup and perfume
- Electrical equipment and appliances
- Valuables
- Home goods or kits
- Household/medical/laundry supplies
- Kitchen items
- Emergency supplies
- Hobby-related items
- Gifts
- Seasonal items
- Home decor/furniture

☐ **Pile** collected items from one subcategory at a time in one place in your home

☐ **Choose** what sparks joy and send everything else off with a "thank you"

☐ **Store** items that spark joy (until the final category of your KonMari Tidying Journey is complete, all storage is considered temporary and flexible)

☐ **Gather** sentimental items from this category and save decision-making for later

☐ **Collect** unused boxes and objects that can be creatively repurposed for storage or decor

☐ **Discard/recycle/donate/sell** items that don't spark joy

Komono Action Items

Things that Spark Joy for Me	Things that DON'T Spark Joy for Me

What did my clutter teach me today?

MINDFUL TO-DO'S

☐ Complete activities related to letting go of "joyless" items (listen to sparkjoypodcast.com *Episodes 42-44: Sell Your Clutter Part I-III* for tips)

☐

☐

MINDFUL SHOPPING LIST

☐

☐

☐

☐

☐

Assessment (Komono)

On a scale of 1 to 10, how do you feel overall about your productivity?
(1 being not productive at all, 10 being extremely productive)

| 1 | 2 | 3 | 4 | 5 | 6 | 7 | 8 | 9 | 10 |

Are you happy with the progress you've made?

What was the most memorable part of joy checking KOMONO?

What were the three biggest lessons you've learned by exploring KOMONO?

What sparked the most joy today?

How are you feeling physically? Emotionally? Mentally?

How are you feeling about your ideal lifestyle? Does that vision seem clearer/more attainable now that you've chosen KOMONO that spark joy?

Other notes (jot down thoughts that may present themselves in the coming days):

KOMONO BEFORE & AFTER PHOTOS

"It is not our memories but the person we have become because of those past experiences that we should treasure."
— Marie Kondo

Sentimental Items

Sentimental Items is the final tidying category and the most difficult for some to address. However, by the time you've reached this category you'll have perfected your decision-making ability and "joy meter"—tools you'll need to succeed. Be sure to exercise careful consideration and respect for items in this category and acknowledge any emotions that may surface.

 Listen while you tidy...

For more tips to help you honor your sentimental items, visit sparkjoypodcast.com
Episode 55: Digitizing Sentimental Items.

Take Action

☐ **Pile** collected items in one place in your home (they may stem from any or all of the previous four signature KonMari categories)

☐ **Subcategorize** to avoid feeling overwhelmed. For example:

- Cards and letters
- Journals and scrapbooks
- Awards, achievements, and trophies
- Childhood items
- Photos

☐ **Choose** what sparks joy and send everything else off with a "thank you"

☐ **Store** items that spark joy (until the final category of your KonMari Tidying Journey is complete, all storage is considered temporary and flexible)

☐ **Collect** unused boxes and objects that can be creatively repurposed for storage or decor

☐ **Discard/recycle/donate/sell** items that don't spark joy

☐ **Display** sentimental items in your home to honor your life experiences

Sentimental Items Action Items

Things that Spark Joy for Me	Things that DON'T Spark Joy for Me

What did my clutter teach me today?

MINDFUL TO-DO'S

☐ Complete activities related to letting go of "joyless" items (listen to sparkjoypodcast.com *Episodes 42-44: Sell Your Clutter Part I-III* for tips)

☐

☐

MINDFUL SHOPPING LIST

☐

☐

☐

☐

☐

Assessment (Sentimental Items)

On a scale of 1 to 10, how do you feel overall about your productivity?
(1 being not productive at all, 10 being extremely productive)

| 1 | 2 | 3 | 4 | 5 | 6 | 7 | 8 | 9 | 10 |

Are you happy with the progress you've made?

What was the most memorable part of joy checking SENTIMENTAL ITEMS?

What were the three biggest lessons you've learned by exploring SENTIMENTAL ITEMS?

What sparked the most joy today?

How are you feeling physically? Emotionally? Mentally?

How are you feeling about your ideal lifestyle? Does that vision seem clearer/more attainable now that you've chosen SENTIMENTAL ITEMS that spark joy?

Other notes (jot down thoughts that may present themselves in the coming days):

SENTIMENTAL ITEMS BEFORE & AFTER PHOTOS

"Once the reducing phase is over, it's time to add joy."
— Marie Kondo

Finding Your Click Point

At this point in your KonMari Tidying Journey, you should be surrounded by a mindfully elevated collection of items that spark joy. You've learned to choose your belongings carefully; therefore, you should be left only with the possessions that fit perfectly in your space. This is called your "click point," the moment you realize you have just the right amount of stuff you want and need to feel content.

 Listen while you tidy...

For more tips to help you reach your "click point," visit sparkjoypodcast.com
Episode 79: KonMari-Approved Storage Solutions.

Storing your Joy

Begin to solidify temporary storage solutions and home decor ideas. Fill in built-in storage spaces with the assumption that they can accommodate everything you own. Remember to continue to store items of like category, size, and material together. Continue to inspire those in your household to complete their own tidying experience by modeling your truth!

YOUR KONMARI POWER ZONE

Now that you've narrowed down the items in your home to only things that spark joy, celebrate by creating a power zone filled with purely positive energy. This can be a corner in your home, a nook, a portion of a drawer, a bookcase, a closet or desk—whatever works for you! The only criteria is for it to serve as a place where you can relax and recharge, filled and decorated only with items that you love.

Once you've created this special space for yourself, settle in and reflect on your journey using the following questions as your guide:

On a scale of 1 to 10, how tidy are you now?
(Look back at your starting score to witness your progress!)

| 1 | 2 | 3 | 4 | 5 | 6 | 7 | 8 | 9 | 10 |

What was the most memorable part of your KonMari tidying experience?

In what way(s) have you begun to realize the vision of your ideal lifestyle and living environment?

Do you feel like you're an extension of a home you honor?

What do you know now that you didn't know prior to tidying up your home?

Complete the following sentence. This experience changed my life in the following ways:

"As long as everything has a place where it belongs,
a certain amount of clutter is not a problem."
— Marie Kondo

Maintenance

Daily tidying practices:

✧ Return things to their proper place

✧ Thank items as you use them or let them go

✧ Clean

✧ Take good care of the things you value

✧ Appreciate the joy that surrounds you (inside and outside of your home)!

 Listen while you tidy...

For more tips to help you stay tidy once and for all, visit sparkjoypodcast.com
Episode 41: How to Maintain a Tidy Home Post-KonMari.

Tidying Maintenance Plan

Now that you've tidied your home using the KonMari Method™, it is *highly* unlikely that you'll rebound to a state of disorder. You're more conscious about what you purchase and bring into your home. You've dedicated many hours to practicing the art of physically putting things away and mentally exercising your ability to make decisions through a lens of joy. Your external environment is in order; therefore, you have no choice but to examine your inner state. Finally, you've zeroed in on your ideal lifestyle, which impacts the way you maintain and respect your home.

That being said, we all have seasons in our lives when we get really busy, our housekeeping gets pushed down the priority list, and our homes become temporarily cluttered. Don't confuse this with a rebound! Rebound is the state in which things without a designated storage place begin to inundate your home all over again. As long as you can eventually find a moment to return your space to its proper state, you have not experienced a rebound.

If you feel that things are getting out of control—do not panic! Return to basics.

Here are some specific tips that will help you maintain your tidy home and avoid rebound:

◇ Mentally return to the lifestyle you envisioned. Refer back to this journal to remind yourself of your progress

◇ Return to your personal power zone and ensure it's in order

◇ Carve out 30 to 60 minutes of unobstructed time to address temporary clutter (trash, folding, putting items in their place, etc.)

◇ If you discover some of your clutter doesn't have a designated place, determine the root cause. Has there been a significant life event that led you to increase the number of things you bring into your home? Have you slipped back into an old buying pattern due to an external influence?

◇ Express appreciation for the contribution your belongings have made to your life and joy check any categories that may have temporarily returned to a cluttered state

◇ Be grateful for the things you have and cherish them

Congratulations!

You've completed your special, one-time KonMari Tidying Journey with the help of *The Tidy Home Joy Journal*. You're officially a For the Love of Tidy Graduate of Tidy! THANK YOU for welcoming this tool into your home and life and for taking action!

So now what?

Join The Spark Joy Club and find your tribe.
Get your your unique, burning tidying questions answered in our exclusive Facebook community.
Visit: facebook.com/groups/thesparkjoyclub

Share your joy and gratitude through the gift of feedback.
Share photos of you putting **#thetidyhomejoyjournal** into action via social media
(tag: **@fortheloveoftidy**).

Mindfully shop hand-selected, simple organizing solutions that spark joy.
fortheloveoftidy.com/tidy-tools

Lean on our trusted network of partners for supplemental help regarding cleaning services,
digital scanning/archiving, and more.
fortheloveoftidy.com/partners

Most importantly, now that you're done with tidying, it's time to get to living! **Relax and enjoy your home and your best life!**

Notes

Notes

Notes

Made in the USA
Coppell, TX
06 September 2020